Omaka's Knights of the Sky

A Guide To The Great War Exhibition At
The Omaka Aviation Heritage Centre

Omaka
Aviation Heritage Centre
MARLBOROUGH • NEW ZEALAND

Published 2013 by The New Zealand Aviation Museum Trust,
(trading as Omaka Aviation Heritage Centre), Blenheim, New Zealand

ISBN 978-0-473-25306-6

Printed by Blueprint Media Ltd, Christchurch, New Zealand

FORWARD

There's something magical about the early days of aviation. For me it is the flying during the First World War that has always captured my imagination. It was perhaps the last era of chivalry and this was no more evident than in the aerial jousting between young men who'd not long swapped their cavalry mounts for aeroplanes.

My own interest in the history of flying during the Great War goes back a long way. I remember being deeply drawn into the classic 1960s movie 'The Blue Max' starring George Peppard. When I was 12, I travelled to England with my parents and was treated to a visit to the famous Shuttleworth Collection, a living museum displaying several original First World War aircraft still in flying condition. On that same trip, I bought a pair of RFC pilot's wings from a flea market in St. Albans. As I grew older I began to acquire other aviation artefacts from the WW-I era. A small collection of uniforms, medals and logbooks grew to include propellers and other aircraft parts until eventually, in the mid 1990s, I had the opportunity to buy a Sopwith Camel in the USA.

I have subsequently been fortunate to be able to assemble a broader collection of aircraft and memorabilia, such that it has allowed us to put together this display to try to convey some of the amazing stories of what these young men were asked to do during an extraordinary time in history. I hope that the displays afford visitors a sense of the time and the experiences, as it is only by 'putting ourselves in their flying boots' that we start to gain a sense of what it must have been like to be a First World War 'Knight of the Sky'.

Peter Jackson

CONTENTS

A DREAM TAKES FLIGHT

The Development of the Omaka Aviation Heritage Centre

Omaka Aviation Heritage Centre was born of a love of aviation, an appreciation of its role in history and recognition of its value to our future.

It began with a resurgence of heritage aviation interest in Marlborough in the mid 1990's when a group of enthusiasts imported two Chinese Nanchang trainers and established the Marlborough Warbirds Association as a way to foster interest and provide a social network of support.

The sound of the Nanchangs' radial engines was heard over Blenheim drawing curious spectators and, increasingly, other heritage aircraft.

As word of the growing range and rarity of aircraft stored at Omaka spread, tourists also began knocking on the hangar doors.

At this point, in 1997, a small group of aircraft owners and enthusiasts got together to discuss the means by which these aircraft could be made accessible to the public on a more practical and sustainable basis, and grow the public understanding and appreciation of aviation. It culminated in the formation of the New Zealand Aviation Museum Trust (NZAMT). Their vision was that this facility should be a focal point of activity reaching not only aviation but also tourism, education and industry, to the benefit of the Marlborough community, New Zealand and aviation enthusiasts throughout the world.

That vision has taken shape as a permanent living centre of aviation heritage designed to fascinate, educate and inspire visitors of all ages. It forms the nucleus for a broader centre of aviation excellence extending beyond the walls of the museum out into the adjoining airpark and businesses using the historic Omaka airfield.

Key to the development has been strong

support from the Marlborough District Council and Marlborough Regional Development Trust, both of which recognised aviation as a key driver in Marlborough's economy and successfully applied to New Zealand Trade and Enterprise for a Major Regional Initiative grant to build Stage One.

The original group of enthusiasts whose dream this was are still very much a part of the ongoing governance and development of the Omaka Aviation Heritage Centre. More have been attracted to join them, particularly in running the Centre's major fundraising event, Classic Fighters Airshow every second Easter. However one individual must be singled out.

Sir Peter Jackson had been drawn to the activities of fellow early aviation enthusiasts at Omaka and quickly became a part of the formation of the NZAMT. At that time he owned just three WW1 aircraft, well before he became 'Sir Peter'. His genuine delight and enthusiasm for the creation of an aviation museum was infectious and added to the determination of the group to see it through to completion.

By the time the facility was finally built in 2005, Sir Peter made an offer too good to refuse. His collection of Great War aircraft and artefacts had grown to the point where he could fit out the entire building and he was willing to do so.

Along with his collection came creative expertise that would be the envy of any museum. A team of contractors from the movie industry was brought together by WingNut Films and began working on ideas formed in consultation with the NZAMT. Magnificent dioramas were constructed and then populated by amazingly lifelike mannequins created by Weta Workshop. The result is the stunning Knights of the Sky exhibition described in the following pages.

It should be remembered that this exhibition displays a private collection and does not attempt to encompass every theatre of conflict nor give even weight to every aircraft, country or individual. It is the presentation of one collection and the stories those objects can tell of that momentous time in history, at the very dawn of military aviation.

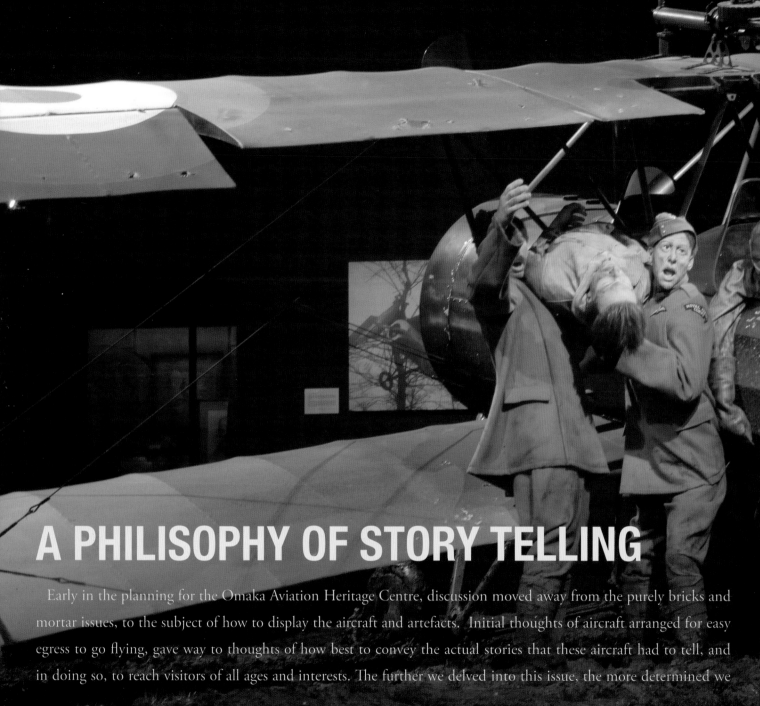

A PHILISOPHY OF STORY TELLING

Early in the planning for the Omaka Aviation Heritage Centre, discussion moved away from the purely bricks and mortar issues, to the subject of how to display the aircraft and artefacts. Initial thoughts of aircraft arranged for easy egress to go flying, gave way to thoughts of how best to convey the actual stories that these aircraft had to tell, and in doing so, to reach visitors of all ages and interests. The further we delved into this issue, the more determined we

became to avoid creating a 'warehouse full of machinery' with rows of similarly placed aircraft behind a velvet rope.

Having made the decision to base the first displays purely on the Great War period, the discussions then centred on just what stories to tell, and how best to represent those historical vignettes in a manner that was accurate, respectful, but also palatable to the public. The fact that Sir Peter Jackson, one of the world's most capable storytellers was a key part of the team meant that the possibilities were endless.

One of the things that Peter was keen to do was to place an aircraft in a tree! This was initially going to be the first thing the visitor saw when entering the display, involving one aircraft, its pilot looking towards the ground as if to say, "I survived the crash, but how am I going to get down from here?" The idea emerged, inspired by a James Dietz painting, to bring together the Nieuport in the tree, with the victorious German pilot, having landed alongside, to portray the bond between fellow airmen, so recently in a battle to the death, but now united as fellow aviators, whilst the German soldiers are excluded as mere spectators of this 'private aviators' club'.

The display of Keith 'Grid' Caldwell about to leap from the wing of his SE5a just before its crash near the trenches is very popular. We were keen to have a New Zealand story as part of the display. This episode features the country's highest scoring 'ace' in a dramatic, true story that also allowed us to discuss Caldwell's impressive career spanning two world wars, and also his philosophy of running a squadron like a rugby team, investing time and guidance to bring younger pilots up the ranks and provide them with the experience necessary to acquit themselves well in battle.

The aircraft displays comprise some very significant original machines from the period, as well as many reproductions. We make no apology for this as the use of full-size representations has allowed us to display aircraft like the de Havilland D.H.2 and the Halberstadt D.IV, both airworthy and both of which cannot boast surviving originals anywhere. In fact, the Halberstadt is the only representative example of that model worldwide. Another benefit in the use of reproductions of early aircraft is the ability to immerse such aircraft into deep dioramas that would be unthinkable using original artefacts. Perhaps the most significant display depicts the last flight of Manfred von Richthofen. This is presented adjacent to the most remarkable display of von Richthofen's personal artefacts, recording his successes in the air and in the hunting field.

'The Red Baron' crashed near the small French town of Corbie on 21st April 1918, and it is a poignant reminder that the battles these aircraft were involved in often ended with young men losing their lives. The Wingnut Films team has recreated the site of the crashed Triplane just as it was described on the day by Air Mechanic Alfred Boxall-Chapman of 3 Sqn., AFC. As Australian troops rush to remove souvenirs

James Orphan

from the crashed Fokker Triplane, von Richthofen's body lies beside the wreck, his over-boots being removed by another of the souvenir hunters. As visitors circle the display of soldiers tearing souvenirs from the wreck, taking in what seems to

be a scene from a movie, their attention is drawn to one soldier using his bayonet to remove the cross from the starboard side of the fuselage. It is then pointed out that the actual cross cut from that side of the fuselage on that day can be seen beside them in the adjacent archway. The mood of the visitors changes palpably with the realisation that this is not a Hollywood stage set but rather, the portrayal of a very real incident from nearly a century ago. This represents a very powerful moment in the experience of the visitor to the AHC. There is suddenly the sense of a very real connection with a moment in history. For many visitors 'The Red Baron' is such a legendary character that he seems to belong more to fiction than to reality. During that moment when visitors embrace the reality of that original cross on the wall, 'The Red Baron' suddenly seems to come to life as a real person and it is ironic that it would take his death scene to bring this about.

During the planning of the display, some discussion ensued regarding the wisdom or correctness of portraying the dead body of a famous identity, and whether or not it would offend anyone. After some debate it was decided that our job was to honour these men and their stories faithfully, warts and all, rather than to try to 'sugar-coat' them. So the display does feature the fallen Baron beside his crashed aircraft. This has affected people in many ways, but after six and a half years and 180,000 visitors, we have not fielded a single complaint about this poignant display.

There are some aspects of the exhibition that do raise questions from time to time. Some visitors have asked why the German side of the conflict is so strongly represented. In essence, the museum is fortunate to have roughly as many German aircraft and as much German memorabilia as it has representations of Allied aircraft and artefacts. We feel that this is an even-handed balancing of the story of the Great War in the air and are happy with the way it is presented. It did highlight however, the fact that most visitors from British Commonwealth countries and also from the USA, are used to seeing aviation collections dominated by Allied aircraft and this is simply the result of there being so few Axis aircraft to display when museums were being established some years after the end of World War Two.

We feel extremely privileged to be in a position to present such an even-handed representation of the combatants in this remarkable four-year conflict. Hopefully, we will be able to do similar justice to the telling of the stories of the Second World War when the time comes.

"... from the first, the light, fast single-seater scout was my ambition. To be alone, to have your life in your own hands, to use your own skill, single-handed, against the enemy. It was like the lists of the Middle Ages, the only sphere in modern warfare where a man saw his adversary and faced him in mortal combat, the only sphere where there was still chivalry and honour. If you won, it was your own bravery and skill; if you lost, it was because you had met a better man."

Cecil Lewis

Brad Hurley photo

15

THE GREAT WAR ABOVE THE TRENCHES

An overview of the 1914-18 War in the Air

Original posters make clever appeals for the war effort.

Original artworks are displayed throughout the memorabilia cabinets, supporting the artefacts with some evocative imagery. 'Mud In Your Eye' by James Dietz depicts a Sopwith Camel which has made a forced landing alongside Allied trenches. The shaken pilot is being offered a tot of brandy by the troops.

Mention the Great War and most people will visualise the wretched life of a soldier in the trenches of the Western Front… mud, rats and the threat of gas, amid the deafening thunder of massed artillery, the call to each soldier to go 'over the top' across no man's land and face the barbed wire and merciless machine gun fire of a similarly entrenched enemy.

Men from over 150 countries fought in WW1, many concentrated in a narrow strip of land that stretched from the Belgium coast to Switzerland. They fought for four long years and 9 million died. When you consider the implications, the photographs of the devastation and the hollow look in those men's eyes, the overwhelming feeling is one of despair at the sheer waste of it all.

Yet there is another story to that conflict, one that is no less lethal but one that is also inspiring. The Knights of the Sky exhibition is a window on quite a different war, in a new theatre fought thousands of feet above those trenches.

Aviation was still in its infancy at the outbreak of war. The Wright Brothers' first flight was in December 1903 but despite considerable advances, flying was still a daring novelty, confined to the wealthier classes. Tens of thousands of spectators would turn out to events where these fragile machines would be pitched in competition against one another or flown in death defying demonstrations to amaze the crowd.

Amongst the military establishment, few recognised the aeroplane's potential. In 1910 the British Secretary of War famously stated "we do not consider aeroplanes will be of any possible use for war purposes". Likewise, the French General Foch commented "aviation is a good sport, but for the Army it is useless"

The early aircraft themselves did little to

counter this impression, being too fragile to withstand vigorous manoeuvres and lacking the power to carry a useful payload.

Nevertheless most of the major powers established a flying corps as an adjunct to their military forces. Numbers were initially low, with serviceable aircraft being fewer than 800 on either side, but this rapidly changed as demand and manufacturing stepped up. By war's end, military aircraft numbered around 20,000.

Initially the chief function of aircraft was as the eyes of the Army. Formerly it had been the job of the cavalry to act as scouts and determine the whereabouts of opposing forces. However the static war that developed in late 1914 made such movement on the largely flat ground impossible. It was necessary to get up into the air to have any chance of seeing what was going on.

Observation balloons were one solution. They were tethered well behind the lines and provided useful vantage points. However, aircraft were mobile and could seek out the enemy, fly right over their trench positions and spot changes to the build up of supplies

in the rear. Information gathered by scouting aircraft soon persuaded the generals of their value to the Army. Aircraft began to be used not only to scout out enemy positions but also to take aerial photographs of the front. Photography was a developing science, which was put to valuable use in the war. Millions of images were produced, creating montage maps of the front.

As aircraft could spot enemy installations, so too could they report on the accuracy of shelling and thus the direction of artillery fire from above became another core role of the flying corps, made practical by developments in wireless communication.

Aviation's emerging roles went hand in hand with developments in capability not only in related technology, but in the aircraft themselves. War created the need and technology found the solutions, increasing engine capacity, improving aircraft design and enabling more potent armament. Aircraft began to specialise.

Reconnaissance, artillery ranging and photography made up the bulk of aircraft operations and required stable platforms.

Naturally they were prime targets, so each side developed aircraft to act as their defenders, accompanying them on missions or hiding several thousand feet above ready to pounce on any would-be attacker. In contrast with the reconnaissance biplanes, these machines needed to be fast and agile, and the single-seat fighter was born.

Instability became a virtue in a fight when abrupt changes of direction could mean the difference between life and death, but handling these aircraft demanded a high skill level from a pilot. One of the most successful fighters of the war was the British Sopwith Camel, but its inherent instability and the vicious torque from its rotary engine made the Camel notoriously difficult for a novice to fly, resulting in a very high accident rate. In the hands of an expert, however, it was superb.

With the fighter aircraft came the 'aces' - pilots whose score of downed aircraft made them famous amongst a civilian population eager for heroes. The expression was coined in France but also used by the Germans who were particularly aware of the effect they had on morale. The British establishment were more reticent, preferring a team approach but media and the public saw to it that fighter pilots were singled out.

Designers continued to push the envelope of aviation design, seeking out the qualities needed in an aircraft that would give their side the edge.

One of the most significant technological developments during the early part of the war was the ability for a machine gun to fire forward through the aircraft propeller. Prior to this, a machine gun might be mounted on the upper wing, firing outside the propeller arc, or an observer would have a rear facing machine gun (both can be seen on the Morane-Saulnier BB). The desirability of a pilot to be able to point his whole aircraft at the target and shoot was obvious, and there were many designers working on the solution. The first practical application came by placing deflector plates on the propeller, so that any bullets that chanced to strike would ricochet harmlessly away. French aviator Roland Garros had such a device fitted to his Morane-Saulnier Type L and

via Paul Sortehaug

achieved three victories with this in April 1915, before being forced down behind enemy lines, where he and his aircraft were captured.

Aircraft designer Anthony Fokker inspected the captured deflector device but he already had his own system under development to control firing by use of a mechanical cam. Fokker's system was probably based on the designs of Franz Schneider who already had an existing patent, but despite the doubtful legal position, Fokker's use of this new technology for his Eindeckers gave Germany that edge which allowed them to achieve

New Zealander, Major Keith Caldwell is seen here second to left, with some of 74 Squadron's central figures, London Colney, March 1918. The RFC and RNAS often included a mixture of nationalities and New Zealand did not have its own air service during WW1. LtoR: Capt Mannock, Maj Caldwell, Lt Roxburgh-Smith, Lt Everard (Adjutant), Lt. Kiddie and Capt Young.

19

Period photograph of a Jasta 12 airfield.

firing with the propeller rotation, the British turned to pusher aircraft like the D.H.2 on display, where the propeller and engine were to the rear, so the pilot could fire forward unhindered. Against such foe, the Eindecker was found to have its limitations as a fighter and its supremacy was short lived. So too was the German monopoly on synchronisation systems and by mid 1916 these were in general use in a variety of forms, the most superior being the Constantinesco gear with which all the British aircraft were eventually fitted.

Innovation was not limited to engineering. Tactics were another key ingredient in determining which side had the upper hand. As combat in the air was an entirely new discipline, it was up to the early pilots to experiment and learn through trial and error. Some individuals proved to be leaders in this field, studying and distilling the lessons they had learned into a system for others to follow. Lanoe Hawker and Oswald Boelke are examples of such men. The generals also drew on that experience and began to develop more efficient means of

aerial supremacy during a period known as the 'Fokker Scourge'.

Not yet having a system to synchronise

using aircraft. As the war progressed, aircraft operations became more closely integrated with Army attacks and aircraft were called upon to fly ground strafing and bombing missions in direct support of the infantry. In the latter stage of the war, German fighter aircraft were heavily outnumbered. They overcame this by combining groups of four specialised fighter units (Jastas) into a Wing or Jagdgeschwader and attacked specific areas to temporarily gain control of the air at a vital point, rather than spread their resources too widely. The most famous of these units was Jagdgeschwader 1, led by Manfred von Richthofen and known among the Allies as his 'Flying Circus'.

Aerial bombing also developed over the course of the war from opportunistic attacks with hand-held devices, such as grenades, small bombs and anti-personnel darts known as flechettes, to aircraft equipped with bomb racks and ever increasing payloads. Their use was largely limited to tactical targets as requested by the Army but most countries also undertook long-range strategic bombing. The most famous example of strategic bombing was the Zeppelin raids on England. Terrifying though they were, the total damage and loss of life was limited. Overall, the impact of aerial bombing during WW1 was constrained by range, payload and accuracy, but the concept was well developed and bombing, both tactical and strategic, emerged as a vital role for military aviation, foretelling its extensive use in the Second World War.

Military aviation began the war as a largely experimental and (to some) an incidental sideshow, but the rapidity of technological progress within the pressure-cooker of a world war saw it grow and emerge as an independent force, demanding of respect and status alongside the traditional forces of the Navy and Army. It is unthinkable today to consider a war without air power.

Furthermore the successful development of aviation during the war ensured it would be taken up on the civilian front and the post-war years were to see an era of record-breaking and trail-blazing flights that would bring air travel to the masses.

THE EXHIBITS

MORANE-SAULNIER G

The Morane-Saulnier company was founded by brothers Leon and Robert Morane in partnership with friend Raymond Saulnier. Developed in 1912, their Type G succeeded in taking out a number of competitive prizes in pre-war Europe. Once war broke out, the aircraft was pressed into military reconnaissance duties for France and her Allies, with a number of manufacturers obtaining licenses to build the type. However, rapid technological developments soon relegated the unarmed Morane-Saulnier G to training duties.

It would fall to Imperial Russia to be the major operator of the Morane Saulnier in combat and continue operation of the G/H family longer than any other nation.

Russia began receiving Morane Saulnier Gs in 1913 and license manufacture was taken up by the Duks factory in that same year.

The Morane served in the front line until 1915, primarily as a reconnassiance aircraft, but also being subject to some bizarre modifications in order to make it more

The Morane-Saulnier at rest on Omaka's grass airfield before it was installed in the museum foyer.

combat effective.

Pyotr Nesterov fitted his Morane G with a long serrated blade which swung down from the rear skid frame. Although this device proved impractical, Nesterov became the first person to claim an air to air victory in WW1. On 25th August 1915, flying a Morane Saulnier G, he rammed an Austrian Albatros B.II. Unfortunately Nestrerov was thrown from his aircraft and died of his injuries.

The action depicted in the museum foyer, is that of Aleksander Kozakov, who devised a weapon consisting of a cable and grappling hook wrapped in explosive cotton. He was actually successful in downing his opponent,

25

and lived to tell the tale, as described in the accompanying panel.

Further wartime fame can be attributed to the Morane Saulnier G as the forefather to a family of combat aircraft developed and used to great effect by the Central Powers.

Anthony Fokker copied the Morane G/H in one of his earliest designs, the Fokker M5. The M5 was a precursor of the famous Fokker Eindecker, whose almost complete air supremacy during 1915 earned it the title of the 'Fokker Scourge' before more advanced Allied fighters were introduced.

An original Morane-Saulnier G survives in the Museo del Aire de Cuatrovientos in Madrid.

The Morane-Saunier G in the Omaka Aviation Heritage Centre was created specifically for this display and is owned by the Trust. It has been built to airworthy standards using aircraft grade construction methods and materials, so that at some point in the future it may be fitted with a suitable engine and flown as part of the Trust's goal to fly more WW1 aircraft at Omaka in support of the wonderful interior dioramas.

Aleksandr Kozakov

Colonel Aleksandr Alexandrovich Kozakov (1889-1919) was the highest scoring Russian 'ace' of the Great War with 20 confirmed victories.

In 1915 he engaged in one of the most outrageous aerial combat experiments undertaken during the war, when he attempted to down an enemy aircraft using a grappling hook!

This was at a time when few aircraft were designed to carry any armament and Kozakov chose to use a grappling hook suspended below his Morane Saulnier. As Kozakov is quoted as saying: *"The damned anchor got caught and was dangling under the bottom of the enemy plane, so I decided to strike across the upper surface of the Albatros with the undercarriage of my plane. I pushed the elevator down and collided. My landing gear folded up into my fuselage and then something blew up with a loud whistling noise."* The hook also had an explosive device attached to it!

An eye witness, Ensign Ivan Smirnov, wrote: *"They flew on for some minutes like this (connected), but then the German lost control and fell to earth like a sack, dragging Kozakov. Disaster seemed very near. Hardly 200 feet from the ground, they seemed to disentangle: a miracle! [Kozakov] tore his machine out of the deadly downward course and landed rough but safely...His opponent...dived his nose into the ground. He became our prisoner."*

This incident is recreated in the museum foyer with a full-sized replica Morane Saulnier Type G.

After the revolution Kozakov joined the joint British Military force at Murmansk, given the rank of Major. He commanded the newly formed Russian Air Division and was awarded the British Distinguished Flying Cross. However it became apparent that the Bolsheviks were winning the war and Britain decided to withdraw its forces from Russia.

On the evening of 1 August 1919, ignoring an invitation to a farewell dinner for British pilots, Kozakov took off in a Sopwith Snipe only to crash to his death a few moments later. Whether this was an accident or if Kozakov chose to end his life, has been the subject of speculation, but we are unlikely to ever know the truth.

Period photograph of Kozakov standing in front of his Morane-Saulnier G. The damaged prop suggests this was taken after the incident described.

CAPRONI CA. 22

Italian Time Capsule

James Orphan

Count Gianni Caproni was the first Italian to establish an aircraft manufacturing factory. Caproni was known as an innovative creator of aircraft for many uses, both civilian and military, commencing with the Ca. 1 of 1910. During the First World War, Caproni built a range of very capable multi-engined bombers, later producing some very large aircraft like the Ca. 90 biplane of 1929, which was the world's largest aircraft at the time.

Introduced in 1914, the Caproni Ca. 22 was configured as a parasol monoplane, meaning that the wings were perched above and separate from the fuselage, just like a lady's parasol or umbrella. A number of monoplanes had already been designed and built by Caproni, like the Ca. 20 which was a mid-wing configured fighter aircraft. What was particularly innovative about this Ca. 22 was the ability to tilt the wing to increase or decrease its 'angle of attack', varying the

angle at which the wing surface met the oncoming air, and thus varying the amount of lift produced. The aircraft was otherwise conventional for the time and was powered by a Le Rhône 80 hp rotary engine.

Serving as a two-seat observation aircraft the Ca 22 flew with the Italian Army's No.15 Squadron which had been using Bleriot monoplanes before the Ca 22 was introduced in April 1915. It is known that seven examples were issued to the Squadron and it is thought that this may have been the total number of Ca 22s built. Initially operating near Piacenza with No.III Group, the Squadron was commanded by Captain Umberto Rossi and conducted reconnaissance flights. On June 30th, the Squadron's aircraft were disassembled and transported to Pordenone near the Austrian border. From there they continued to carry out reconnaissance flights as well as commencing bombing operations over enemy territory.

Little more is known about the history of the Ca 22s. The example displayed here

The Caproni is complete, including its original Le Rhône rotary engine.

James Orphan

30

is the sole survivor and until recently, was the property of the Caproni Museum, established by Gianni and Timina in 1929. This machine could be described as a virtual 'time-capsule' as it has changed very little in the past 85 years, most of it spent in storage, so it is a very great privilege to be able to display it here at Omaka.

Francesco Baracca

Like many pre-war officers, Count Francesco Baracca began his military career in the cavalry. He learned to fly in 1912 at Reims and was serving with the Battaglione Aviatori as a experienced pilot when Italy entered the war on the Allied side in May 1915.

Fighting along the Austro-Hungarian border, Baracca's (and incidentally Italy's) first aerial victory was in a Nieuport 11 single seat fighter on 7th April 1916. He went on to fly the Nieuport 17 and later the SPAD VII. Baracca was ultimately credited with 34 aerial victories and was Italy's top scoring Ace.

In June 1918 he failed to return from a mission and reports came in of a crashed aircraft on fire. His remains were later recovered and it was apparent that he had died from a single bullet wound to the head.

Adorning all of Baracca's aircraft since mid 1916, had been an emblem taken from his old cavalry regiment, that of a black prancing horse. In later years, his mother presented this emblem to Enzo Ferrari and the black stallion continues to grace the famous Italian automobiles to this day.

This period photograph shows Baracca standing proudly before his Spad VII and its prancing horse insignia.
An original painting of Baracca by Ivan Berryman is on display in the museum and a tribute was paid to him during the 2009 Classic Fighters Airshow. Items belonging to other Italian airmen are displayed in the Allied memorabilia section.

ETRICH TAUBE

Igor Etrich's Remarkable Dove

At the time war broke out in Europe, Austrian designer Igo Etrich's elegant Taube had already been a successful aircraft for four years, having first flown in 1910. Harking back to the centuries of man wanting to 'fly like a bird', the Taube (Dove) has the distinction of being the most bird-like of any successful aeroplane ever built. Described as stable and pleasant to fly with a creditable performance from the 100hp Mercedes engine most commonly fitted, the Taube had by 1914 even been built as an enclosed cabin touring monoplane putting it well ahead of its time. The most common derivative however was the two-seat military version developed in 1912 by Rumpler and by the time that war broke out on 4th August 1914, the type was in widespread service with Germany, Italy and Austro-Hungary.

With the opening of hostilities the German military immediately found these

Despite its bird-like appearance the Taube's wing was actually modelled on the Alsomitra macrocarpa seed pod, which can be dispursed by the wind for up to ten kilometres.

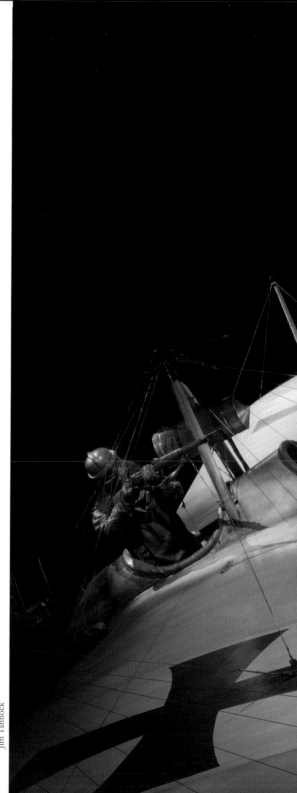

Jim Tannock

Early aircraft, such as the Taube, were ill equipped for combat. This German observer positions his rifle between the bracing wires to take a pot-shot at an approaching British Be.2

graceful old machines, and they were considered old at the time, to be ideally suited as aerial observation posts for monitoring enemy movements. Such was their value at the front that many privately owned aircraft were impressed into military service and further factories were seconded to produce the design, Tauben eventually being furnished by as many as 10 different manufacturers.

A primitive feature of the Taube which was common to many early aircraft but which was all but gone by the end of the Great War was the provision to 'warp' the wings, effectively twisting the entire mainplanes in order to bank the aircraft to the left or right, much as a bird can be seen to do in soaring flight. By 1914, most designers had already

air changed from an emphasis on passive observation to one of aerial combat and the unarmed Taube soon became outclassed by dedicated fighting scouts sent to knock out those 'flying lookouts'. By the end of the first year of fighting the Tauben had all been pulled back to serve out their senior years as training aircraft.

By the time production ceased, approximately 500 Tauben had been completed including a number of 'Stahltauben' distinguished by their steel tube fuselages replacing the original wooden structures. By the end of the First World War a small number of these machines had survived to ultimately find their way into national museums in Europe. More recently a handful of faithful reproductions have been completed including this one, built in Furstenwalde, Germany by a small team led by Heinz Linner, appropriately another Austrian. First flown on 13th May 2000, it made a number of flying appearances at airshows in Germany before being shipped to New Zealand in late 2005.

moved to the use of 'ailerons', (hinged surfaces at the trailing edge of the wing which move up or down to influence the banking movement) which have remained the standard system ever since.

Technological progress during wartime must necessarily be brisk and very soon after the commencement of the conflict, the whole complexion of the war in the

MORANE- SAULNIER TYPE BB

French company Morane-Saulnier was a prolific designer and manufacturer of aircraft of all configurations during the First World War period and for many years afterwards. Best known for its various

This scene depicts an ambulance being hailed to assist a downed airman. It is obviously too late for his observer in the rear cockpit. During the war Red Cross volunteers from around the world established base hospitals, nursing and rehabilitation services, as well as caring for the welfare and eventual repatriation of POWs. The size of the organisation grew exponentially, as evidenced in America where 1 in 5 citizens was a member of the Red Cross by 1918.

monoplane designs, Morane-Saulnier also produced the Type BB biplane.

Constructed in 1915 under a contract order of Britain, the Morane-Saulnier Type BB was a small two-seat biplane. Intended for the reconnaissance role, the aircraft carried a crew of two, pilot and observer. The original order was for 150 aircraft equipped with the 110 hp Le Rhône rotary engine, but because of the shortage of this powerplant the majority of the 94 machines constructed were powered by the smaller 80hp Le Rhône. The type saw limited use with the French Army and three Royal Flying Corps squadrons were briefly equipped with the Type BB, however it was soon phased out of service in favour of more capable aircraft.

Remarkably, one example of this little known aircraft did survive, albeit in incomplete condition, the disassembled fuselage, undercarriage and rudder being held in store by the RAF Museum Reserve Collection, Satafford, England. The aircraft displayed here is a reproduction and is presently the world's sole intact example.

James Orphan

FOKKER E.III 'EINDECKER'

Ironically inspired by a French racing aircraft, the Fokker E series of monoplanes proved to be well ahead of their time when introduced in mid-1915. Their speed, agility and revolutionary through-the-propeller machine gun fire capability provided an advantage that outclassed Allied aircraft during a period which became known as 'The Fokker Scourge'.

The Fokker E.III was the most successful variant of the Fokker 'Eindecker' (meaning one-wing or monoplane) series of fighting scouts of the First World War. Designed by Dutchman Anthony Fokker it was the first type to arrive in sufficient numbers to form specialist fighter units in early 1916. Previously Eindeckers were allocated singly to the front-line 'Feldflieger Abteilungen' that carried out reconnaissance duties. On 10 August, 1916, the first German Jagdstaffeln (single-seat fighter squadrons) were formed, equipped with the E.III.

The E.III was basically an upgrade of the earlier E.II fitted with larger, newly designed wings. It retained the same 100 hp Oberürsal U.I engine but had a larger 21.5 gallon main fuel tank which increased the aircraft's endurance to over 2½ hours, an hour more than its predecessor. Most E.IIIs were armed with a single Spandau lMG 08 machine gun with 500 rounds of ammunition, however after the failure of the twin-gun Fokker E.IV as a viable successor, some E.IIIs were fitted with twin guns.

Fokker production figures state that 249 E.IIIs were manufactured, however a number of the 49 E.IIs were upgraded to E.III standard when they were returned to Fokker's Schwerin factory for repairs.

The E.III entered service on the Western Front in December 1915 and was also supplied to the Kaiserliche Marine and to Austria-Hungary for service with the army and navy. Turkey was supplied with 22 E.IIIs, some of which were based at Beersheba in Palestine while others operated in Mesopotamia during the Siege of Kut-al-Amara.

The 'Fokker Scourge' ended after greater numbers of more capable fighting aircraft were introduced by the Allies. These included the antiquated looking but very successful British Airco D.H.2 pusher biplane, the French Nieuport 11 biplane and the Morane Sauliner Type N 'Bullet' also of France and very similar in appearance to the Eindecker.

By late summer 1916, rapid advances in aircraft technology saw the remaining Eindeckers pulled back from front line service and relegated to training duties.

James Orphan

Max Immelmann & Oswald Boelcke

Oberleutnant Max Immelmann

Hauptmann Oswald Boelcke

Two of Germany's first 'aces' of the war, both Immelmann and Boelcke had been educated at military schools and after initial wartime service, transferred to the Luftstreitkrafte. Both proved to be capable pilots and in July 1915 were amongst the few chosen to fly the revolutionary new Fokker Eindecker. As their tallies grew, a friendly rivalry began, with first one and then the other holding the leading score.

Immelmann, who developed a manoeuvre that still bears his name, the Immelmann turn, was the first pilot to be awarded the Pour le Mérite, Gemany's highest military honour. The medal was unofficially known

Max Immelmann's pocket watch and Pour Le Mérite commemorative silver cups.

as the "Blue Max" in his honour. Both Immelmann and Boelcke were decorated with Pour le Mérite medals on the same day.

Immelmann met his death on 18 June 1916 during a dogfight with seven British aircraft. Credit was awarded to RFC pilot McCubbin and gunner/observer Waller but controversy still remains, as German authorities claimed he fell to anti-aircraft fire, while others believed the synchronisation gear failed and Immelmann shot off his own propeller. At his death he was aged 25 with 17 victories.

The death of Immelmann prompted authorities to restrict the flying of their other hero Oswald Boelcke, in the interest of public morale. He spent a period advising on military aviation and set out his analysis of fighter tactics in a rulebook known as 'Boelcke's Dicta'.

After a tour of Turkey and the Russian front he was recalled and asked to establish a fighter squadron. He had permission to hand pick his pilots and amongst those chosen was Manfred von Richthofen.

Boelcke ensured his new Jasta was disciplined and drilled in his combat rules. He deployed them in the first ever attempt at gaining local air-superiority, moving away from the lone wolf style of earlier fighter-scouts to the teamwork of hunting in packs.

His legacy of codifying and teaching aerial tactics lived on well into WW2 and earned him the title of 'the father of aerial combat'.

Boelcke was killed in October 1916 as a result of a mid air collision with fellow pilot and friend Erwin Böhme, illustrating the consequences of violating one of his own rules, that two aircraft should not attack the same opponent. He was 25 when he died and had a total of 40 victories.

A portrait of Oswald Boelcke in a commemorative frame, shaped like a Prussian pilot badge, alongside a gift plate with engraved signatures including Immelmann, Ritter, Fromm and Schilling.

Objects associated with Immelmann and Boelcke are displayed adjacent to one another. Here can be seen several commemorative trophies including one presented to Immelmann's mother following his death. In the centre is a pennant presented at the funeral of Boelcke by British Officers who were prisoners of war. Beneath this is a desk set which was a Christmas gift from Boelcke to Immelmann in 1915.

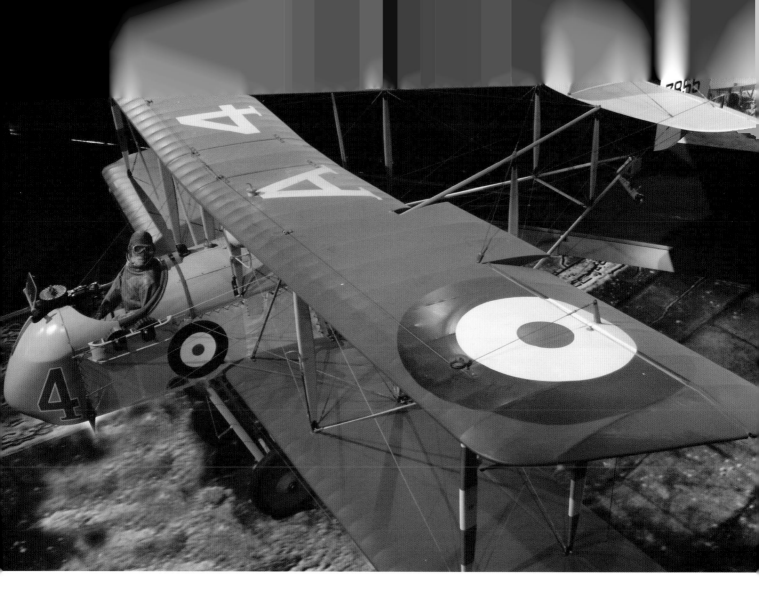

AIRCO DE HAVILLAND D.H.2

While its ungainly looks may give it the appearance of the earliest styles of flying machine, Geoffrey de Havilland's D.H.2 was in fact one of the first of a new series of military aircraft, the 'fighting scout' or what would eventually become known simply as, a 'fighter'.

When the D.H.2 first appeared in the skies over the front, more modern looking de Havilland designs such as the B.E.2 series had been in operation for many months, in fact since before the war even started. By reverting to the 'pusher' configuration the goal was to produce an aircraft that could fire a machine gun forwards without the risk of hitting a turning propeller. Some two-seater designs were still flying in this configuration, including the larger and similar looking D.H.1a, however the D.H.2 was designed to be an agile single-seater in which the pilot could point the whole aircraft towards his prey and fire the .303 inch Lewis machine gun directly at it rather than swing a moveable gun towards his target. The most effective way to produce this effect at the time this machine was on the drawing boards was to place the engine and propeller behind the pilot, thus requiring the open 'birdcage' style aft fuselage arrangement.

First flown on 1 June 1915 the D.H.2 went through a number of trials to determine its suitability for service at the front before production commenced. The first D.H.2s arrived for squadron service in France in February 1916. At that time the dominant fighter on the front was the modern looking Fokker E.III 'Eindecker' monoplane which was the first German type to operate with a machine gun synchronised to fire between the revolving propeller blades. Despite the obvious advantages of the German monoplane, the antiquated looking D.H.2 proved itself a worthy adversary and helped level the odds in the skies over France. The aircraft became popular with pilots for its light controls and its agility. All aerobatic manoeuvres could be performed and the 100 hp Gnôme Monosoupape provided ample power. With the forward-most seating position the field of view was exceptional, one contemporary D.H.2 pilot remarking that flying the aircraft was "like riding a witch's broom"!

A total of 451 D.H.2s were completed by the Aircraft Manufacturing Company (Airco). Approximately 300 of these saw combat in France (along with others in Macedonia and Palestine), and they acquitted themselves well in service. Those serving in France saw front line service until the withdrawal of the last examples in July 1917. Survivors were then employed on training duties until 1918. Sadly, not a single example is known to have survived beyond a few years after the end of World War One.

Since then a handful of reproductions have been completed. The aircraft here on display is fully operational and has been built full size and to a very high standard of accuracy with only the type of engine differing from the original unit.

The D.H.2 flying in the skies above Omaka. Photo: Gavin Conroy

Lanoe Hawker

Major Lanoe Hawker was the first British Ace of the war and the first pilot to be awarded the Victoria Cross for aerial combat.

He gained his Aviators Certificate in March 1913 at his own expense and transferred to the RFC in August 1914. His early flying was on Henri Farmans and then B.E.2cs. It was in flying the latter that he earned a Distinguished Flying Cross for a solo attack on the Zeppelin sheds in Gontrode using hand grenades.

Hawker proved to be an aggressive, skilful pilot as well as a crack shot. His Victoria Cross came in 1915 after a triple victory, a rare feat in those early days. He was also inventive, succeeding with innovations ranging from improved machine gun feeds to fur lined 'fug boots'. At the start of 1916, Hawker lead the RFC's first fighter squadron (No.24) flying D.H.2s, which helped to counter the supremacy of the Fokker Eindeckers. However as innovations continued and the D.H.2 was itself surpassed, the days were numbered in which Hawker's skill alone could overcome

the difference. When Hawker came up against Manfred von Richthofen in 23 November 1916, Hawker was flying the now obsolete D.H.2, while his opponent was flying the more powerful Albatros D.II equipped with twin Spandau machine guns. Nevertheless the lengthy dogfight that ensued has gone down in aviation history.

"First we circled twenty times to the left, and then thirty times to the right. Each tried to get behind and above the other. Soon I discovered that I was not meeting a beginner. .. He was travelling in a machine which turned beautifully. However, my own was better at rising than his, and I succeeded at last in getting above and beyond my English waltzing partner." Manfred von Richthofen

After close to 30 minutes of constant tricks and evasion in which Hawker's aircraft lost more and more height, he was finally forced to run for the lines. He became Richthofen's 11th victim, shot through the head and dying instantly. The victory cup can be seen in the Richthofen section.

German soldiers buried Hawker near Bapaume but his grave was never found. He was 26 years old, with 7 victories.

Hawker's motto was "Attack Everything!" Pictured below is the No.24 Sqn Operational Orders for 20 July 1916, signed by Hawker. This is on display in the Allied Memorabilia section.

MEMORABILIA

Approved designs signed off for RFC wings, badges and buttons.

Items belonging to British ace 'Mick' Mannock, who was posthumously awarded the Victoria Cross.

Franks Luke's compass, the 'unseen gift'.

Within the Centre are two areas of Memorabilia, one devoted to the Allies and the other to the Central Powers. The main Allies were France, Britain, Belgium, Russia, Italy and the USA, all bar one having uniforms on display. In particular there are the uniforms of the top scoring Allied ace Frenchman René Fonck (75 Victories) with his Croix de Guerre and 26 Palms, and the top scoring American ace Eddie Rickenbacker (25 Victories). On display are also artefacts related to other Allied aces: Rhys Davids, McCudden, Mannock (Britain), Collishaw (Canada), and Clayton Knight, Luke and Werner (USA). The latter two made a speciality of destroying enemy balloons and there is a particularly poignant item relating to their last flights.

Of particular interest is the large display of what is called 'trench art': broken or used items of propellers, shells, etc. which have been turned into clocks, photograph holders or merely pieces of art.

A section of the Memorabilia displaying items from American involvement in the War, including some from Escadrille Lafayette the famous French squadron of US volunteers.

A collection of beautifully crafted 'sweetheart badges'.

Mark III Thornton Pickard built Hythe Machine Gun Camera, designed to replicate the shape, weight and operation of a Lewis gun for training pilots in air-to-air combat.

Early pre-war pioneering aviation is represented by a remarkable collection of items, most being associated with Louis Bleriot, who was the first to fly the English Channel in 1909.
At right can be seen a 1908 fabric covered Bertin & Boulline compound lifting and stabilising propeller (mounted above like a helicopter but with a tractor propeller in front). The curious lattice-like structure to the rear is actually a radiator panel from a Bleriot X prototype.

Oak plaque from St Omer, the most famous British airfield in France.

Uniform of top scoring Allied ace, Frenchman René Fonck, with Crois de Guerre medal and 26 palms

'A Pilot's Luck' book by Clayton Knight, signed by some of the most notable names in early aviation.

A section of German Memorabilia showing one of the many original paintings which adorn the displays. Here can be seen an Ivan Berryman painting 'Josef Jacobs' portraying the German Ace with his distinctive black Fokker Triplane. Beneath is a photo of Jacobs in a silver frame made from an Ehrenbecher honour goblet.

Freidrich Christiansen was credited with 21 victories flying a seaplane during WW1. An impressive collection of medals, trophies and uniforms spans his service through both wars.

Wicked anti-personnel darts known as flechettes were dropped on the infantry.

A selection of magnificent trophies belonging to Manfred von Richthofen including a presentation goblet on his award of the Pour le Merite order.

Ernst Udet's Pour Le Mérite' medal.

A personal seal belonging to Count Ferdinand von Zeppelin is among the many Zeppelin related artefacts, spanning the pre-to post war period.

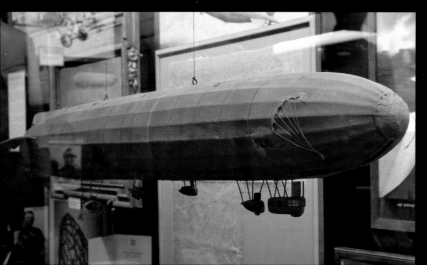

In the Central Powers section (Imperial Germany, Austro-Hungaria, Bulgaria and Turkey) uniforms and medals of these countries are also on display. The Germans in particular were lavish in the commemoration of their top airmen and there are numerous items of cups and display items belonging to them. Artefacts of Boelke, Immelmann, Christiansen, Goering, Udet, Jacobs, Konnecke, Schafer and of course, Manfred von Richthofen, the highest scoring Fighter pilot of them all with 80 Victories. Also on display is an item belonging to the top scoring gunner Ehmann (25 Victories). There are even four 'Pour le Mérite' medals among the collection, (nick-named The Blue

Max) which was Imperial Germany's highest decoration for bravery in WW1.

In both sections can be found pieces of actual fabric taken from shot down aircraft as well as the stories of some of the famous

pilots of the time. There are also items that pre and post-date the war, including a remarkable selection of early pioneering aviation items and others associated with the giant German dirigibles and flying boats.

Herman Goering was the third and last commander of JG 1, the famous Richthofen Flying Circus. In this section of memorabilia, Goering's handwritten log book from WW1 is displayed, together with a number of items from both world wars, most notably the officer's cap he was wearing when he surrendered to US Forces in 1945.

To the right can be seen a display of items belonging to Ernst Udet, together with paintings and a large scale model of his Fokker DVII, carrying the name LO! on the fuselage in honour his girlfriend Eleonore.

BREGUET 14.A2

Taking a break from rearming the Lewis guns, a soldier relaxes with a pipe on the far side of the Breguet exhibit.

One of the most successful aircraft of the war, the Breguet 14 was a robust machine, which still managed to be light and manoeuvrable due to its innovative construction. Over 8,000 machines were ultimately manufactured in reconnaissance, bomber and post war civilian variants.

An unusual feature of the aircraft was the wide use of Duralumin with only the wing ribs and fuselage fairings being wooden. An initial batch of 580 Br 14.A2 reconnaissance

models were ordered in April 1917 and at this point in time the prototype Br 14.B2 was built and delivered, this being the bomber version.

The Br 14 was much in demand during the last years of the 1914-18 war, which resulted in the production of 5,500 before the war ended, this including both types. Both versions were armed with a forward firing Vickers gun for the pilot and Lewis guns for the observer. The observer's Lewis gun was mounted on a French Etévé ring – similar to the British Scarff ring. Some A2s had a Lewis gun mounted on the top wing in place of the Vickers and a downward firing Lewis for protection from below and for trench strafing (the first recorded gunship). The A2 carried 4 small bombs, a camera and a wireless set. The aircraft has dual controls.

The Breguet 14 was supplied to 71 French escadrilles (squadrons) on the Western Front, five escadrilles in Serbia, three in Greece, six in Morocco and eight in Macedonia as well as two Belgian escadrilles. 229 A2s, 47 B2s and 100 E2 trainers were supplied to the American Expeditionary Force (A.E.F.) in

James Orphan

1918. The aircraft were widely used for both day and night bombing in the last year of the war.

The aircraft on display is a replica depicting an aircraft of the 12th Photo Section of the A.E.F. 96th Aero Squadron. The unusual, almost 'metallic' paint finish was carefully researched from original fabric samples and recreated by The Vintage Aviator Ltd (TVAL) technicians here in New Zealand. Other improvements included the installation of a Scarff ring and Lewis gun along with the fixed Vickers gun, all these items created very accurately in-house at TVAL.

Two original examples are known to survive, one in France, the other in Finland.

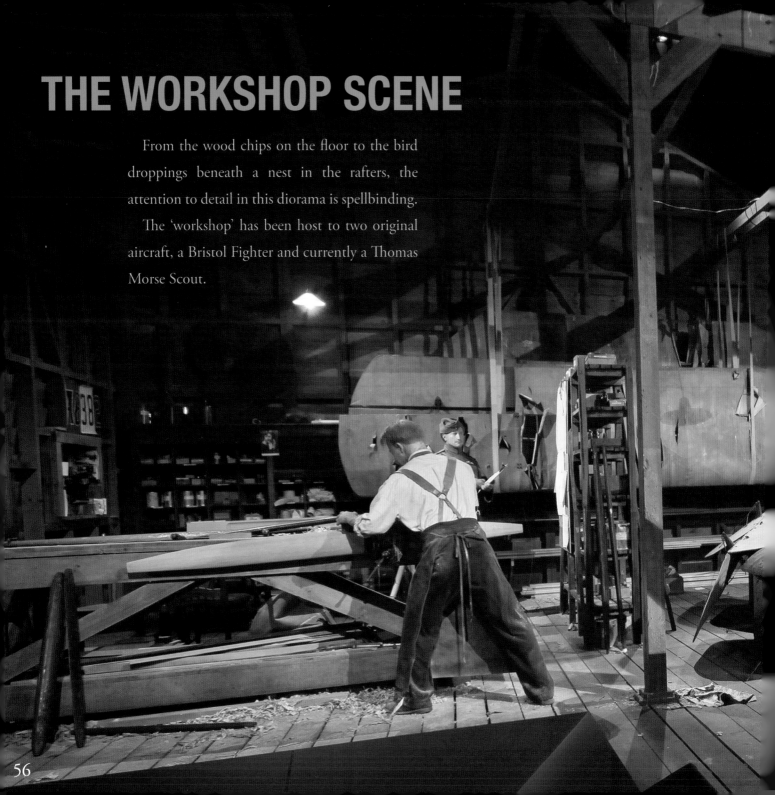

THE WORKSHOP SCENE

From the wood chips on the floor to the bird droppings beneath a nest in the rafters, the attention to detail in this diorama is spellbinding.

The 'workshop' has been host to two original aircraft, a Bristol Fighter and currently a Thomas Morse Scout.

THOMAS MORSE SCOUT

The Thomas-Morse Scout or 'Tommy' became the standard single-seat advanced trainer used by the U.S. Air Service during the Great War, fulfilling its role in America prior to the graduate pilots being posted overseas.

In January 1917 the Thomas Company, founded by a young Englishman who had emigrated to the United States, merged with the Morse Chain Company and would thereafter become the Thomas-Morse Corporation. The first aircraft to be born out of this union was a single-seat biplane, designated the S-4. The fuselage featured a wooden, wire-braced, box girder construction, with a rounded top decking, all of which was covered with fabric, as was the slender wooden empennage. The staggered wings were supported by wooden interplane struts and were constructed of wood, wire-braced and fabric-covered.

Ailerons were fitted to the top wings only, these being operated by vertical pushrods.

Powered by a 100 hp. Gnôme Monosoupape 9-B rotary engine, the aircraft first flew in June 1917 and proved to be a gentle, but responsive aircraft, although it did not have the attributes needed to be a front-line fighter. It was thereafter offered up for consideration to both the U.S. Army and Navy. It was the Army who placed the initial order of 50 machines, just prior to the U.S. entry into the Great War. These were powered by a 110 hp Gnôme and redesignated S-4Bs. The U.S. entry into the war saw an additional 100 examples ordered.

Some problems were encountered with the 9-B rotary, and it was decided to fit the last 50 of the Army order with the reliable 80 hp. Le Rhône 9-C. This, and a slightly shorter fuselage and shorter span wings, saw a new designation, the S-4C. In all 447 Le Rhône versions would be delivered, and the Thomas-Morse Scout or 'Tommy' became the standard single-seat fighter trainer used by the U.S. Air Service during World War I.

Post war the Air Service sold the aircraft as surplus to civilian flying schools, sportsman pilots, barnstormers and ex-Army fliers. Some were still operating into the mid-1930s starring in WWI aviation movies, such as 'Hell's Angels' and 'Dawn Patrol', appearing in the guise of British, French and German aircraft.

Little is known about the aircraft seen here displayed in 'time-capsule' condition. It would appear that the 'Tommy' received extensive modifications to the forward fuselage, most likely in the 1920s, to widen the cockpit area to accommodate a second occupant, this alteration resulting in the removal of the distinctive cowling 'cheeks' so often associated with these machines. It is believed to be one of only 10 survivors.

The simple instrument panel shows the patina of decades in storage.

Period tools line the workshop's far wall.

CURTISS MF FLYING BOAT

Glenn H. Curtiss is perhaps best remembered for his perfecting of the seaplane, he being among the first to experiment with pontoons and flying boat hulls. His earliest models were built and sold from 1912, but it wasn't until the following year that they were given the designation 'Model F'. Curtiss would go on to produce around 150 'F-boats' for a worldwide market particularly for Russia, Japan, Italy, France and England.

Curtiss delivered a total of 22 to the U.S.Navy before the initial contract was terminated with the Armistice in November 1918. The Navy's fleet of 'F-boats', used almost entirely for training, remained essentially unchanged from the original design dating from 1912-13, however by 1918 an improved model was needed, which resulted in the Model MF (Modernised F-boat). Powered by the 100-hp Curtiss OXX6 it had many improvements, including sponsons borrowed from the Curtiss 'America' flying boat, which greatly

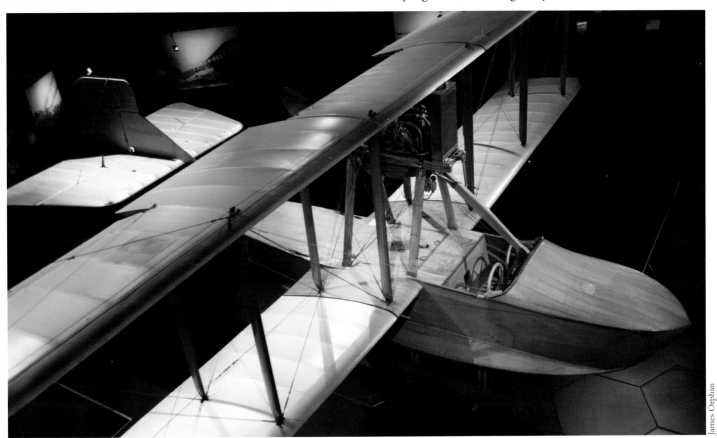

improved planing and stability, along with a revised, unequal-span wing layout that incorporated ailerons into the upper wings.

The MF was deemed to be an excellent trainer and the Navy decided to order 80 more from the Naval Aircraft Factory at Philadelphia, which had been created in 1917 to build Curtiss types under licence to keep up with demand. The MFs were delivered in 1919-20, and whilst some saw operational service with the Fleet they were in the main delivered to Naval Training units, some going straight into storage due to the post-war downsizing of the service.

Many of these aircraft were subsequently sold as surplus and the Curtiss Company converted others to what became known as the MF 'Seagull', which mainly involved engine changes to increase horsepower and seating to accommodate additional passengers. A variety of engine options were available, of which the 150-hp Hispano-Suiza and 160-hp Curtiss C-6 were the most numerous. Several were used by commercial operators for charter work and mail runs, and some were involved in 'rum running'

during the Prohibition. Perhaps the most notable feat performed by the MF was as a camera platform to document the Amazon during the Alexander Hamilton Rice Expedition to Brazil during 1919-20. This example survives with the Canada Aviation & Space Museum.

The beautiful example you see on display at Omaka (c/n NC 903 and US Navy A-5543) is one of only four examples known to exist. Manufactured by Naval Aircraft Factory at its facility in the Philadelphia Navy Yard it was the 61st built from a batch of 80. Little is known of this boat's early history but it was almost certainly operated at a Naval Aviation training station and thereafter released for sale as surplus sometime in the early 1920s. It appears to have been operated for joy rides by William H. Long in the Cleveland, Ohio area and was donated by him following refurbishment to the Cleveland's Frederick C. Crawford Auto-Aviation Museum in June 1945.

The NZ Flying School

At the outbreak of WW1, there was no formal programme available within New Zealand to train for the Royal Flying Corps. Brothers Vivian and Leo Walsh looked to provide such a service.

Vivian Walsh had made the first powered, sustained, controlled flight in New Zealand in 1911 and with his brother Leo went on to build the country's first flying boat. They approached the Government to establish a flying school but without success.

The brothers then took on investment partner Reuben Dexter. Together they established the New Zealand Flying School in October 1915 at Kohimarama, utilising the wide expanse of the Waitemata Harbour as their training ground.

They constructed and operated a number of flying boats, augmented by another ordered from the Curtiss Aeroplane Company in America in April 1916 (an earlier model from the MF on display). They replicated the Curtiss and continued modifying the configuration and engine installations of all their aircraft throughout their years of operation. Amongst their late 1918 fleet were two Boeing Floatplanes, the first two aircraft produced by William Boeing, founder of today's giant aerospace company.

In flight training, the New Zealand Flying School gave priority to those enlisting with the Royal Flying Corps and amongst the first students was Keith Caldwell. Other 'Aces' Mac McGregor and Ronald Bannerman also earned their wings at Kohimarama making up a total of 107 pilots trained between 1915-1923.

Once the Great War ended, demand for training dropped off dramatically. The company struggled with reduced staff. Principal amongst them was George Bolt, who had originally been taken on as an apprentice in 1916 but rose to become chief pilot and engineer. After the war he pioneered mail routes in the region and set a number of distance and height records while at Kohimarama.

Unfortunately the Government still failed to grasp the potential benefits of aviation. Despite their achievements there was little official recognition or support for the Walshes and the school ceased operation in October 1923.

In 1924 the Government agreed to purchase the school's assets and the aircraft were towed across the bay for storage at Devonport. Sadly the graceful flying boats were left to rot and later burned at the waters edge. Speculation as to the fate of the Boeings continues, but they most likely shared the same ignominious end as the flying boats.

ROYAL AIRCRAFT FACTORY R.E.8

Nicknamed 'Harry Tate' after a popular music hall performer, the RAF R.E.8 was considered neither popular nor much of a performer. It was nevertheless built in considerable numbers and proved a necessary if not ideal workhorse.

This two-seat biplane reconnaissance and bomber aircraft was intended as a replacement for the vulnerable pre-war B.E.2, however the R.E.8 was little improvement and is regarded as one of the worst aircraft designs of the war. The first of two prototype R.E.8s (Reconnaissance Experimental 8) flew on 17 June, 1916 and the first production aircraft reached France in November of that year. However, early aircraft were prone to spinning, resulting in a number of accidents and the R.E.8 was grounded while a larger tailfin was designed. The R.E.8 was not a popular aircraft with aircrews, at best being described as 'workman-like.' Although it was a good platform for artillery spotting, the aircraft had little chance at out-manoeuvring enemy fighters. An example of this occurred on 13 April 1917 when a patrol of six R.E.8s from No. 59 Squadron RFC was met by aircraft from Jasta 11 and all the R.E.8s were shot down within five minutes. Despite such massacres the R.E.8 did claim several aerial victories through defensive fire.

The R.E.8 eventually equipped 18 Royal Flying Corps squadrons from 1917 and Belgium was the only country other than Britain (and her Dominions) to operate the R.E.8, receiving twenty two in July 1917. Eventually 4,077 R.E.8s were produced and

they served in most theatres including Italy, Russia, Palestine and Mesopotamia. Just two R.E.8s survived the ravages of time and these are displayed in museums in London and Brussells. The aircraft displayed here is a reproduction built here in New Zealand exactly to the original 1916 specifications.

Two of Weta Workshop's mannequins provide a sense of drama to the tableau. The observer mans the Lewis guns to fend off an attack, as the aircraft patrols above a pock-marked landscape.

The kewpie doll inside the letter 'D' for doll as carried on the side of A4397, flown by Captain R.G. Francis of 3 Sqdn Australian Flying Corps. This Re.8 had the distinction of holding the highest flying hours (440) in the British Forces.

James Orphan

STRATEGIC BOMBING

Long-range bombing to disrupt the enemy's economic ability and public will to fight, was carried out within days of the outbreak of WW1, with a Zeppelin attack on Liege in Belgium, while the Russians set up specialist units as early as August 1914 with the first heavy bomber of the war, the huge Ilya Muromets. Other nations employed limited strategic bombing but generally avoided civilian targets.

Zeppelins began bombing England from January 1916, followed in 1917 by the fixed wing G-class heavy bombers, like the Gotha and the R-class giants. Although damage and loss of life were sustained during the attacks, the more significant effect was the realisation that Britain was vulnerable, and this resulted in valuable resources being diverted away from the Front to be used in home defence.

Limited strategic bombing was carried out by the British, particularly by the RNAS but in June 1918 a dedicated unit was established as the Independent Force. It primarily utilised D.H. 9s and Handley Page 0/400s. Although strategic in intent, in practise however, its operations were more often directed towards closer tactical targets in support of the army.

Limited range, too few aircraft, light bomb weight and poor accuracy all conspired to

Scale models of the British Vickers Vimy and German Gotha bombers are representative of strategic bombing during the Great War.

reduce the overall impact of strategic bombing. Nevertheless, the concept was well developed and if the duration of the war had been extended, better aircraft and plans by the Allied forces to launch large-scale cooperative bombing raids, might have changed the equation. Strategic bombing emerged as a leading component in the vision for any future conflict, paving the way for what was to come in WW2.

Gotha G.IV

The Gotha was the mainstay of the German strategic bomber programme. It was the G.IV that participated in the bombing of London and other locales in southern England once the Zeppelins were countered by better aircraft and incendiary bullets.

Built in numbers, and arriving at the Front in April, 1917, the G.IVs were to carry out several raids on London before defences improved and the burgeoning weight of the aircraft equipment reduced attack altitude. By September 1917, Hauptmann Brandenburg, leader of the main bombing squadron, was forced to reduce the operations of the Gothas to night missions only.

Vickers Vimy

The Vickers Vimy was designed to bomb Germany from its bases in England and first flew on 30 November 1917, but only three of these heavy bombers reached the Independent Force before the Armistice was signed. The Vimy only reached full service status in July 1919 when it entered service with the RAF in Egypt. The aircraft was the main heavy bomber force for most of the 1920s. The Vimy served with the Royal Air Force in the Middle East from 1919 until 1925, when it was replaced by the Vickers Virginia, and in Northern Ireland until 1929. The final aircraft (a training aircraft based in Egypt) was withdrawn in 1933.

However its main claim to fame occurred after the war had finished, when Vimys were used to win a series of prizes for long distance flights. The first was in June 1919 when Alcock and Brown flew the first transatlantic flight. Then in November Ross and Keith Smith flew from England to Australia followed by Brand and van Ryneveld, who flew from England to South Africa.

ROYAL AIRCRAFT FACTORY S.E.5a

The S.E.5 may never have achieved the iconic status of the Sopwith Camel with which it is always compared, but it was a capable and robust fighter and proved to be one of the most important and influential aircraft of the war.

The original S.E.5 first flew in November 1916 and entered operations over the Western Front with No. 56 Squadron RFC in April 1917. Only 77 original S.E.5s were built before the improved S.E.5a model replaced it. The introduction of the 200-hp (149 kW) Hispano-Suiza or Wolseley Viper resolved the earlier engine problems and added nearly 30 mph (45 km/h) to the aircraft's top speed.

The S.E.5a entered service in June 1917 and by 1918 equipped 21 British Empire squadrons as well as two U.S. squadrons. The aircraft proved to be inherently stable, making it an excellent gunnery platform and was also one of the fastest aircraft of the war. While it was not as agile as the rotary-engined Camel, it was far easier and safer to fly whereas the Camel had claimed a large number of allied airmen in accidents. It is worthy of note that many of highest scoring Allied 'aces' including Billy Bishop, Raymond Collishaw, 'Mick' Mannock and James McCudden, enjoyed their greatest successes flying this type. Legendary British ace Albert Ball was initially disparaging of

the S.E.5 but in the end scored 17 of his 44 victories flying it. McCudden wrote of the S.E.5 "It was very fine to be in a machine that was faster than the Hun's, and to know that one could run away just as things got too hot." Highly respected Irishman Edward 'Mick' Mannock VC, DSO, MC, the highest scoring British pilot, achieved 50 of his 73 aerial victories flying the S.E.5a.

In total 5,205 S.E.5s were built by six manufacturers including Austin Motors and Vickers. After the end of World War One, the S.E.5a enjoyed continued service for a time including participation in the new novelty of skywriting in the U.K. as well as service in the USA where small numbers of the type were built under licence.

Just six original S.E.5 series aircraft survived, however a number of very fine reproductions have been completed including this completely authentic New Zealand produced example. Here it is used to tell the remarkable true story of 'Grid's Great Escape', as detailed in the following pages.

'GRID' CALDWELL

A New Zealand National Hero

A story to make all New Zealanders proud is that of Kiwi pilot Keith 'Grid' Caldwell. A successful combatant and highly respected leader, Grid Caldwell became New Zealand's highest scoring ace with 25 aerial victories to his credit.

The display shows an amazing episode in Caldwell's story in which he managed to regain control of his S.E.5a fighter after it was crippled in a mid-air collision, managing to stabilise it by placing himself half in and half out of his cockpit for just long enough to nurse it back to the lines and jump clear just as it was about to crash. Caldwell survived his fall and the war, and was C.O. of RNZAF Base Woodbourne for the first half of the Second World War!

James Orphan

70

THE SNOW SCENE

Easily the most photographed exhibit at the AHC is the 'snow scene'. Here we see a Royal Flying Corps Nieuport biplane that has been damaged in a dogfight with a German Siemens-Schuckert. The Nieuport has crashed in a large tree and the pilot has managed to clamber down where he is greeted warmly by the German flyer who has landed nearby.

The two pilots share a cigarette as German soldiers look on, all of them standing in a thick carpet of snow to produce what must be one of the most dramatic museum displays to be seen anywhere.

James Orphan

SIEMENS-SCHUCKERT D.IV

I t wasn't pretty, but as a fighting machine the Siemens-Schuckert D.IV was as potent as anything developed by the warring nations of the First World War. It just arrived at the front a little late in the conflict to really make an impression.

Siemens engineers produced an aircraft weighing no more than its predecessor, the D.III, but with a reduced wing area and a much higher combat performance. The latter was mostly due to a new engine, the 200-hp Siemens Haiske SH.IIIa. The engine was unique among rotaries in that the crankshaft revolved in one direction

James Orphan

and the cylinders and crankcase revolved in the opposite direction, thus giving an equivalent engine speed of 1,800 rpm with a propeller speed of 900 rpm, a direct 2-I reduction. This feature allowed the use of a huge four-bladed propeller. From the pilot's standpoint the Siemens-Schuckert D.IV was an excellent aircraft; its most notable feature being its phenomenal rate of climb and extremely high service ceiling. The aircraft was easily controlled and very responsive, although according to pilot reports it had a nasty stall, whilst the short landing gear and limited propeller clearance led to tricky landings.

The D.IV started reaching operational units in August 1918, but of the 280 ordered only 123 were completed by the end of the war - about half of those reaching operational units. In October 1918 the aircraft was officially described as superior by far to all single-seaters in use. Production of the D.IV continued after the cease-fire, with many being sold to Switzerland, where they operated into the late 1920s.

No complete original Siemens-Schuckert

James Orphan

D. series fighter has survived, however three reproductions of the D.IV have been completed in recent years. This one flew in the USA for a time before being shipped to New Zealand where it has undergone a major refurbishment to bring it to the very authentic presentation you see today.

NIEUPORT 27

The Model 27 represented the last of a line of very successful and rather similar looking scouts produced by the French Nieuport company and collectively referred to by the Germans as 'Vee-Strutters'.

The Nieuport 27 was a French biplane fighter aircraft designed by Gustave Delage and was the last of the Nieuport 'V-strut' aircraft to see service. Based on the successful Nieuport 17 and 24 fighters, the N.27 incorporated a large plywood vertical tail

and a redesigned, rounded horizontal tail to improve stability. The N.27 also differed from the N.17 in that it featured a more shapely rear fuselage which made use of long wooden stringers to give a rounded shape to the aircraft. Horsepower was improved over the earlier models with the installation of either a 120hp, and occasionally a 130hp Le Rhône rotary engine.

The Nieuport 27 was armed with a synchronised, fuselage-mounted Vickers machinegun and/or a Lewis Gun mounted on a 'Foster mount' above the top wing.

The aircraft served with the French Aviation Militaire and also with the British Royal Flying Corps (later Royal Air Force) during 1917 and early 1918. By mid 1918 however most N.27s had been withdrawn from service and replaced with the Spad S.XIII or the completely new Nieuport 28. Some 120 Nieuport 27 aircraft also saw service with the United States Army Air Service as trainers in 1918.

No original examples of the Models 24 or 27 survive today however several Model 17s are preserved in Europe.

ACES HIGH
The Jasta 11 Display

Jasta 11 was formed on 28th September 1916 but did not go into service until the 12th of October. Led by Oberleutnant Rudolf Lang the new unit failed to achieve a single aerial victory before a replacement Commanding Officer arrived in January 1917.

Manfred von Richthofen - early career

Manfred von Richthofen was born into an aristocratic Prussian family in 1892. He was an avid horserider and hunter, spending time with his brothers hunting wild boar, deer and birds, with the result that the family home was adorned with trophies and celebratory cups, a tradition he continued with his aerial victories.

Following a military education he joined the cavalry, hoping for glory as a young Ulan. However he was disillusioned with the trench warfare that developed and in May 1915 requested a transfer to the German Air Service. He began as an observer during which time he claimed a French Farman shot down, however this was not credited as it fell behind enemy lines. In October 1915 he enrolled for flight training and despite a less than glowing conversion to pilot qualification, he did prevail in the end, initially flying an Albatros C.III two-seater. During this time he made another claim after shooting down a Nieuport, however this also failed to be credited.

A major event in his career occurred when he meet Oswald Boelcke, the celebrated ace and leader of Jasta 2. Von Richthofen was invited to join the squadron and with great admiration for his new CO, Manfred became the most dedicated student of the famous 'Dicta Boelcke' – the 10 key rules established by Oswald Boelcke as an indispensable guide to air fighting. Flying an Albatros D.II, successes with Jasta 2 commenced with the downing of an F.E.2b on 17th September 1916. His 11th and most significant victory came on 23rd November when he won against leading British Ace Major Lanoe Hawker VC. By early January 1917, Manfred's tally was 16 when he was given control of Jasta 11. His story is taken up in the following pages.

Manfred von Richthofen had become an accomplished fighter pilot in the last months of 1916, with 16 aerial victories achieved while flying with Jasta 2, initially under the tutelage of pioneering fighter tactician Oswald Boelcke. The dust had barely settled after Manfred's arrival when on 23rd January he successfully shot down an RFC F.E.8 near Lens.

Leading by example and handpicking his men, von Richthofen quickly galvanized Jasta 11 into the most successful fighting unit on the Western Front. Von Richthofen's

own personal score would double in less than four months.

From January 1917 through to November 1918, Jasta 11 pilots would claim some 350 aerial victories making it the highest scoring Jasta of the war. The title of 'ace' would be conferred upon no fewer than 26 of the unit's pilots. It is little wonder then that this amazingly accomplished fighting unit became so famous on both sides of the trenches during 'The Great War'.

The Triplanes on display are wearing the specific and carefully researched colours of individual machines that were operational with Jasta 11 during March of 1918. During this period the Jasta was being led by Manfred von Richthofen flying his all red Dr.I.

All the aircraft of Jasta 11 were distinguished by the common colour of red for the cowlings, struts and undercarriage on aircraft, which apart from Manfred's, were still predominantly coloured in the streaky olive finish applied at the Fokker factory. Thereafter, each aircraft carried its individual pilot's chosen additional colours.

THE FALL OF
THE RED BARON

The Great War's most famous combatant, Baron Manfred von Richthofen, took to the skies for the last time on the morning of 21st April 1918. During a year and a half of action, he had downed an unbeaten record of 80 aircraft.

The legendary 'Red Knight of Germany' was flying low over the Somme Valley in pursuit of another aircraft when he received a single bullet wound to the chest. He immediately brought his Triplane down in a beet field, managing to get it on the ground with relatively little damage, but he succumbed to his wound almost as the aircraft came to rest.

The area in which the red Fokker came down was occupied by an Australian gunnery unit. As Manfred's body was lifted from the wreckage the troops began to gather souvenirs from the wrecked aircraft. Very quickly, the Triplane was torn to ribbons,

Jim Tannock

82

Soldier mannequins are seen removing souvenirs from the wreckage. The original fabric cross is displayed nearby, while the fur overboots are in the Australian War Memorial, Canberra.

Manfred von Richthofen was buried with full military honours in the French cemetery at Bertangles. His body was later returned to Germany and buried in Berlin, before being moved again to Wiesbaden at the time of the construction of the Berlin Wall.

James Orphan

items removed even including the Baron's distinctive fur covered over-boots

Remarkably, quite a number of items from von Richthofen's Triplane have survived. The engine is displayed in London, the seat in Toronto and the control column in Canberra. Some years after the event, one of the Baron's over-boots was presented to the Australian War Memorial. Incredibly, the second over-boot was also presented to the Australian War Memorial, so that nearly a century after the irreverent taking of these items, they can be seen together once more as a pair.

Among items most sought after by the troops were the black crosses from the wings, fuselage and tail of the Triplane. In the recreation depicted here, a soldier is seen cutting the cross from the starboard (right hand) side of the fuselage with his bayonet. That actual historic piece of cloth has miraculously survived and can be seen in the adjacent archway.

'The Red Baron' was buried with full military honours at Bertangles Cemetery near Amiens. Years later his body was returned to Germany and his grave can now be found at Wiesbaden. Back in 1918 however, there commenced intense controversy over whose weapon actually killed the most famous aerial knight of all time. Credit was initially given to Captain Brown in the following Camel, however detailed forensic investigation eventually transferred the credit to a single Australian gunman, Sergeant Cedric Popkin.

James Orphan

The Richthofen family were keen hunters and their home was adorned with trophies. Manfred von Richthofen continued the tradition by commemorating each of his aerial victories with a small silver cup. Every tenth was of a greater size. On display are numbers 10 and 11, the latter recording his famous victory over the then highest scoring British pilot, Lanoe Hawker, in a duel that Manfred recounts in his autobiography.

Displayed adjacent to the Death of the Red Baron scene is the original starboard fuselage cross, taken from Manfred von Richthofen's crashed Fokker Triplane 425/17 by Lance-Corporal A.E. Putmen.
A close study of the cross, assisted by nearly 100 years of flaking, shows various modifications the Germans made to their national aircraft markings in early 1918. The common curved Maltese cross was replaced by the straight armed Balkenkreuz cross, which itself changed proportions from wide to narrow. All these changes were made to Richthofen's Fokker Triplane since it left the factory in January 1918.

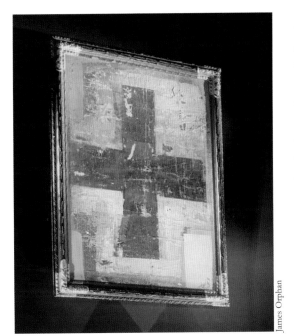

James Orphan

ERNST UDET

The Germans loved and respected Ernst Udet. He was a genuine hero, a record holding airman, a movie celebrity and aviation innovator.

When WW1 ended, he was ranked second only to Richthofen with a total of 62 victories and was the most successful fighter pilot to survive the war.

Born in 1896, the son of a wealthy land owner, Udet had a natural flair for anything mechanical. When war broke out in 1914, he reported to the army with his own motorcycle, to volunteer as a messenger. Although too young for the army, Udet spent a few months riding his motorcycle backwards and forwards behind German lines delivering messages.

He applied for pilot training, and whilst waiting for a response, he learnt to fly at his own expense.

Udet began flying for the German Air Service in August, 1915, flying two-seaters, then fighters, but in a defensive position and rarely encountering the enemy. By December

Bronze statue of Udet

1916, after flying for over 15 months he had only 3 victories, a rather slow start for someone destined to become one of Germany's highest scoring aces.

After requesting a transfer to Jasta 37, Udet's score rose fast during 1917. He earned a reputation as a lone eagle, flying solo against the enemy. On one such flight, he engaged the famous French ace Capitaine Guynemer. The two stalked each other for 8 minutes, then battle began and Udet's guns jammed rendering him defenceless. Chivalry in the skies prevailed and Guynemer withdrew from combat, leaving Udet to fight another day.

After 19 victories and meeting Richthofen, Udet was given command of Jasta 11 in March 1918, flying the Fokker Triplane. Within weeks, Udet had been awarded the Pour le Merite (whilst in hospital with an ear infection), and Richthofen was dead.

In July, Udet was shot down by a French Breguet, but he was wearing a parachute - a luxury afforded some German pilots. However, the harness had tangled with his control coloumn and he barely managed to pull it free as his aircraft spun towards the ground. He jumped from only 300 feet and landed heavily in a shell hole and was rescued by German infantry.

Now commanding Jasta 4 and flying the Fokker D.VII, Udet downed 20 aircraft during the period 3 - 25th August, 1918. His Fokker had a red and white candy striped top wing, a red fuselage carrying the initials of his fiancee "LO", and the inscription "Du noch Nicht!" (Not you yet!), painted in bold letters on his tail as a message for any attacker.

His war ended on September 26th, 1918 when he was badly wounded in the thigh with his tally at 62.

After the war, Udet became a test pilot and toured an aerial circus through the US, thrilling crowds with his acrobatic abilities in the skies. He also found work flying as a movie stunt pilot.

At the outset of WW2, he was persuaded to join the Luftwaffe by his old WW1 comrade Hermann Göring and appointed to the rank of Generaloberst after outstanding service during the campaign against France in 1940.

However, Udet died on 17 September, 1941. The German propaganda machine announced he had died whilst testing a new aeroplane and Hitler ordered a state funeral.

In reality, his position in the Luftwaffe had become untenable due in the main to political infighting, and he had committed suicide in Berlin, using an old Mexican six-shooter given to him in his days as a Hollywood stunt pilot.

He was buried with full military honours.

A rich collection of Udet memorabilia is on display. Amongst them are a hand drawn card, dinner menu, a water colour cartoon and two cigars given to Udet by his Jasta 4 comrades at a special dinner to celebrate his Pour Le Merite award. The medal itself was later lost and Udet was given a display version until a replacement was eventually provided. Both can be seen on display here.

THE BLUE MAX RETURNS

Often described as one of the prettiest aircraft designs to have emerged from the First World War era, the Pfalz D.III also proved a capable combat machine from the time of its introduction. The aircraft displayed here however, enjoyed a very different history, in which it came to be recognized as a movie star!

In April 1917, Pfalz Flugzeug-Werke designer Rudolph Gehringer, produced a new fighter design. The biplane owed much to the earlier work the company had performed building the designs of the Roland company, particularly the use of a moulded plywood monocoque fuselage. Two layers of veneer strips were spirally wrapped in opposing directions over a mould to form half of a fuselage shell. The fuselage halves were then glued together, covered with a layer of fabric, and doped. This method gave the fuselage great strength and smooth contours compared with conventional construction techniques.

The prototype Pfalz D.III first flew in May 1917 and deliveries to operational units, began in August. The D.III was generally considered inferior to the Albatros D.III and D.V scouts in service at the time, contemporary pilot accounts criticising the Pfalz's lack of speed, power, and lack of climb compared with the Albatros. The Pfalz also stalled sharply, spun readily, and slipped in turns, however it was structurally sound and could safely dive at high speeds due to its sturdy, two-spar lower wing (a weak point of the Albatros machines, some falling apart when placed in a steep dive). The strength

James Orphan

of the Pfalz made it a favourite of pilots tasked to shoot down Observation balloons. The only major complaint among the pilots who used it in this role was that the machine guns were buried in the forward fuselage, making it impossible to clear jams in-flight. This led to the slightly modified D.IIIa, which moved the guns to the upper decking.

Some 300 Pfalz D.III and 775 D.IIIa scouts were built but after the war no example was preserved and the type disappeared into history until the late 1960s when the motion picture 'The Blue Max' was produced. The film featured two Pfalz D.IIIs built in England. The principal character was played by actor and pilot George Peppard who spent time in both of the Pfalz scouts during the making of the film. This aircraft was located in poor condition in Alabama, USA in 1999. It was restored here at Omaka resulting in the Pfalz returning to flying condition and wearing the unique lozenge colour scheme created by the producers of 20th Century Fox for 'The Blue Max'.

The Pfalz D.III being flown over Omaka by the late Stuart Tantrum, who had been responsible for the restoration of the aircraft in New Zealand.

Overleaf: The beautiful Pfalz under the spotlights. Photo by James Orphan.

NIEUPORT 24 & THE 'V-STRUTTERS'

So successful was the Nieuport 'V-Strutter' series of biplane scouts that the type was built in various evolving models from the beginning of the war almost to the end, and the designs were also built by other Allied countries - even by the Germans!

The earliest of the Nieuport biplane scouts was not actually built as a combat aircraft but rather as a racer, to be entered into the Gordon-Bennet Trophy contest of 1914. In the event, war broke out and the annual race meeting was cancelled. The racing biplane, known as the Nieuport X, was soon adapted to serve as a military observation machine. The military design became the Nieuport 11 Bébé and the type entered service with France's Aviation Militaire in the summer of 1915. The N.11 was subsequently also

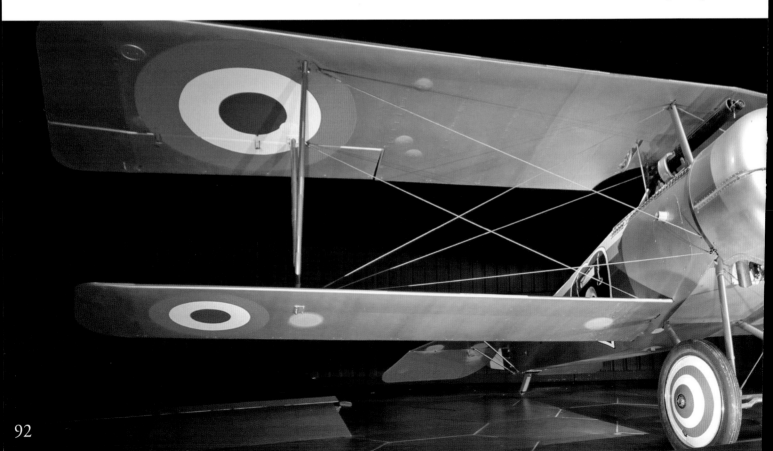

used by the Royal Naval Air Service and the Royal Flying Corps, as well as by Italian, Belgian, Dutch and Russian forces. Further development saw the 80 hp Le Rhône rotary engine replaced with a unit of 110 hp and with increased wing area this became the Nieuport 17.

The popularity of the Nieuport continued with the N.17 which entered service in May 1917, while the customer base grew to include American, Swiss, Swedish and Finnish air arms. The next model to emerge was the N.24, distinguished by its more rounded fuselage sides. Some N.24s retained the older square shaped style of vertical tail while others featured the new rounded tail with its small fixed fin and large moving rudder surface. This model led to the again similar Nieuport 27, the 'last of the V-strutters' an example of which can be found elsewhere in this building. The subsequent Nieuport fighter was the N.28 which was a completely new and very effective fighting scout that remained in front line service right through to the end of the conflict.

Exact production numbers for the Nieuport biplane fighters are difficult to establish since they were manufactured for over three years, not just in plants in France but also in Great Britain, Holland, Russia, Italy (which produced over 500), Japan and even in Germany where a number of facsimile examples were produced by Siemens-Schuckert, not under license, but after being unashamedly copied for use by German forces. This could not have been a better endorsement of the design!

The Nieuport 24 on display is an airworthy replica in the colours of Charles Nungesser. His distinctive insignia reflects his adopted title, "The Knight of Death".

James Orphan

FRENCH ACES

René Paul Fonck

With a total of 75 victories, Fonck was France's highest scoring Ace and also ranked the Allied 'Ace of Aces', a title that remains unchallenged to this day.

Despite his later prowess as a pilot, when Fonck was first conscripted into the military in 1914, he declined joining the air service in favour of becoming a combat engineer in the trenches. He later changed his mind and volunteered for pilot training, joining an observation squadron in May 1915. He quickly demonstrated his aptitude for flying but it was not until he was asked to join the elite Escadrille les Cigognes that his real skills as a fighter pilot were realised.

Flying the SPAD S.VII and subsequent cannon-firing variants, Fonck developed as a disciplined and calculating hunter. He stalked his prey, weighing the odds carefully and striking quickly with an economy of bullets. In this method he was highly successful and on two occasions shot down six aircraft in one day.

Despite his pre-eminent status, Fonck was not a popular man. He seldom socialised with the other pilots but when he did was inclined to boast.

Fonck survived the war and continued flying in demonstrations and racing during the inter-war years, including an unsuccessful long-distance record attempt.

During WW2 his reputation was badly damaged by unfounded accusations of collaboration. He died in 1953 aged 59.

George Guynemer

Shy and frail in appearance, Guynemer would seem to be the antithesis of the hero image, but perhaps because of this he was all the more beloved by the French people.

He had a passionate interest in aviation and despite being rejected for military service on account of his health, persisted in reapplying until he was finally accepted as a mechanic. Gaining entry to pilot training took further persistence, but Guynemer's determination

René Fonck was the top scoring Allied Ace. His uniform can be seen on display in the Memorabilia collection

"until one has given all, one has given nothing"
George Guynemer

saw him earn his wings in April 1915. He was assigned to Escadrille MS.3 and downed his first enemy aircraft a month later. Diligence and practice saw his success grow and with it admiration and national fame. He used his influence to effect a number of technical developments in SPAD aircraft, including the installation of a 37mm cannon to fire through the propeller shaft.

In March 1916 he achieved a triple victory, then a quadruple in May. His chivalrous side was also displayed, when in a famous episode Guynemer called off a dogfight with Ernst Udet when the German's guns had jammed.

Guynemer took part in over 600 aerial combats, achieved 53 victories and was himself shot down seven times before his final fatal flight. On 11th September, 1917 he was declared missing in action, aged 23.

Charles Nungesser

Nungesser was a flamboyant character, whose exploits as a fearless airman, his love of danger, beautiful women and fast cars, together with his dislike for authority, earned him great popularity in France as the embodiment of the handsome Devil-may-care flying Ace. He was known to arrive for a dawn patrol, still wearing his tuxedo from the night before, sometimes with a female companion.

However, his life was far from charmed, as Nungesser suffered injury after injury, incurring multiple fractures, dislocations and wounds during flying and driving accidents. At times he was so incapacitated that he had to be helped into the cockpit.

Nevertheless, Nungesser continued to stack up victories to become France's third highest scoring Ace, with 43 victories by war's end.

Post war Nungesser pursued a series of aviation-related careers, including flying for the movie industry. He met his death in an attempt to be the first to cross the Atlantic Ocean. He and fellow Frenchman Francois Coli set off from Le Bourget Airport on 8th May 1927 in their aircraft 'L'Oiseau Blanc' but were never heard of again. Two weeks later, Charles Lindbergh successfully made the crossing, flying the reverse route from New York to Paris.

The Nieuport 24 on display is in the colours of popular French Ace, Charles Nungesser.

'l'as' (ace) was first used by a French newspaper to describe Adolphe Pégoud, after he became the first pilot to down five enemy aircraft. The concept was widely adopted in order to boost civilian morale and known as Überkanonen 'top gun' by the Germans. It was less favoured by British officials, but soon picked up by the media who were keen to publicise heroes. Indeed the majority of aerial victories were at the hands of relatively few.

HALBERSTADT D.IV

One of the least successful of the German fighting scouts, the attractive Halberstadt 'D' series of aircraft flew well but never quite managed to match the performance of their contemporaries.

The D.IV was Halberstadts' attempt to improve the basic design of the company's earlier fighters, the D.II and D.III. The aircraft was fitted with a more powerful engine and twin machine-guns in order to compete with the products of fellow manufacturer Albatros.

A report from early 1917 illustrates that this was not successful: *"The model IV bears the same classic design of the earlier single seat Halberstadts in this series. In keeping earlier elements within the design, the Halberstadt D.IV has fallen behind the times and can no longer compete with the others that have advanced past this technology. This model has been given a new engine of 150 H.P. That is 30 more than the D.III, but also too little and too late"*

Approximately 110 Halberstadt D.II and D.III's were built during 1916 and 1917, but only three D.IVs were produced. The final model in the series was the D.V of which approximately 90 were produced. All of the 'D' series Halberstadts that served at the front did so between June 1916 and mid-1917, when all were withdrawn to serve in less demanding areas.

The Halberstadt company went on to produce the hugely successful two-seat Halberstadt Cl.II in mid 1917, also based on their earlier single-seat designs. Some 900 of that model were produced and 700

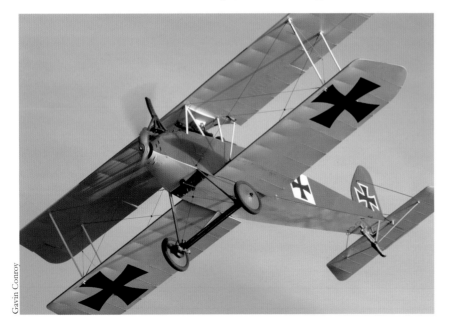

Gavin Conroy

examples of its successor, the Cl.IV were ordered with production still underway when the war ended.

Of the single seat Halberstadt 'D' series, not one example has survived. The machine displayed here is a fully flyable reproduction built in the USA by highly respected WW-I aircraft constructor, the late Carl Swanson, during the 1980s. This is the world's sole representative example of the Halberstadt single seaters.

DE HAVILLAND D.H.4

The most successful aircraft designs of the Great War could perhaps be identified as those which continued in service long after the conflict was over. The de Havilland D.H.4 was such a machine and provided as valuable a contribution in peace time as it did during the war.

The D.H.4 was designed as a day bomber

and general-purpose reconnaissance aircraft. First flown in August 1916, it was subsequently deployed at the front in March 1917. Performance figures were quite impressive and the aircraft was able to operate above the effectiveness of the German fighters during long range bombing sorties over Germany in 1918. It proved vulnerable however during artillery spotting and photo-reconnaissance where it was found to have an 'Achilles heel'. The design saw the 67-gallon (254-litre) fuel tank placed between the pilot and gunner. This not only made communication between the two crew difficult, but if hit by enemy fire or if the aircraft was forced to crash land, both men were in danger of being burnt to death. As a result the D.H.4 became known as the 'Flaming Coffin'.

The aircraft was also an important element of the U.S. Army Air Service both during and after the Great War. Manufactured under license and dubbed the 'Liberty Plane' it was the only aircraft manufactured in the US to serve on the Western Front. Postwar it was employed in a variety of roles

until 1932, including that of transport, air ambulance aerial photography platform and trainer. In addition, the D.H.4 was the principal aircraft used by the U.S. Government when Air Mail service began in 1918 and the type continued in that role for several years. One young pilot who became very adept at flying the harsh Air Mail routes was Charles Lindbergh who became familiar with the demands of flying in the dark, in poor weather and over long distances while flying the D.H.4. This experience would go on to serve him well when he became the first solo pilot to successfully fly the North Atlantic in May 1927.

A total of 1,536 D.H.4s were completed in England during the First World War, however the aircraft on display here is one of 4,840 D.H.4s built under licence in the United States and is one of just two original examples known to survive.

James Orphan

The famous Liberty engine, reputedly designed in just five days after the Aircraft Production Board brought Jesse Vincent of Packard Motor Car Co. and E.J. Hall of Hall-Scott Motor Co. together at the Willard Hotel, Washington and tasked them with drawing up plans for an advanced aero engine as quickly as possible.

US INVOLVEMENT

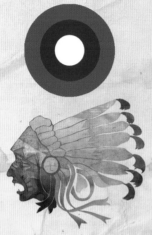

America's military forces were ill prepared for a major foreign war, none more so that the Air Service, although by 1917 it was far stonger than the six aircraft it had in August 1914 when the Great War began!

Although America had been hestiant to declare war, Congress had budgeted for substantial increases in equipment, land for airfields and an expansion of personnel. By the end of 1916 there were plans for no

Before the US officially declared war, some
Americans volunteered to fly with the French in the famous squadron Escardille Lafayette. The Indian head was their squadron emblem, as displayed on several original sections of aircraft fabric amongst the memorabilia. Below can be seen the shooting star of the 22nd Aero Sqn.

fewer than 24 squadrons. However by the time America entered the war not all of these plans were in place, with only the 1st Aero Squadron fully operational.

Nor was the manufacturing industry able to adapt quickly enough with respect to developing new aircraft designs and they therefore turned to using European aircraft and building designs under licence. The most successful was the D.H.4, which was built in large numbers and fitted with an American designed Liberty engine.

It wasn't until February 1918 that the first U.S. squadron entered combat, but this rapidly escalated to 45 squadrons by Armistice Day and despite only nine months of operations they managed a respectable showing, claiming over 750 enemy aircraft for the loss of 289, whilst contributing to 150 bombing attacks.

At war's end a massive demobilisation saw the Army Air Service contracted. America slipped back into its isolation policy which would see it caught unprepared at the beginning of another World War some 23 years later.

Eddie Rickenbacker

Edward Rickenbacher was born on 8th October 1890 in Columbus, Ohio to Swiss parents who had immigrated to the New World as newlyweds. He grew up in austere surroundings and when his father died, Eddie was just 13. He worked at various jobs to raise money for the family before his fascination with machinery drew him into the new automotive industry. By 19 he was working in Dallas as both designer and salesman, and managed to convince his boss that entering cars in racing contests would promote sales. He enjoyed huge success in winning many races and a new careeer emerged. By 1916 he was a celebrity earning $60,000 a year racing cars. While visiting Brooklands in the UK, Rickenbacher discovered a new interest in the RFC aircraft operating from inside the circuit and decided it was time to get into aviation.

After the US entered the war, Richenbacher sailed with the Expeditionary Forces, serving initially as a driver and mechanic, but applied to learn how to fly.

He first ventured across the lines on 6th March 1918 with Patrol Leader Raoul Lufbery and scored his first victory on 29th April. Hunger for action saw him flying 'lone wolf' patrols for several hours a day. He amassed five victories in May and received instant recognition in the USA as the celebrity racing driver who became an 'Ace'. He also changed the spelling of his name to the less 'German' Rickenbacker.

On 24th September be became commander of his unit, the famous 94th Aero Squadron, known by its 'Hat in the Ring' motif. Captain Eddie claimed another six victories that month and an impressive 14 during October, finishing the war with 26.

Having survived, Rickenbacker continued a high profile career and made and lost more than one fortune. During WW2 he went missing with the crew of the B-17 in which he was travelling but survived three weeks in a life raft. A motion picture of his life was made in 1945 starring Fred MacMurry.

After a long, fulfilling life, Eddie Rickenbacker died in Zurich, Switzerland on 27th July 1973.

Eddie Rickenbacker, America's top-scoring ace with 26 victories.

Rickenbacker's own flight suit, which he called his 'Teddy Bear Suit', worn to combat the extreme cold of flying at altitude. Visible are his name and the Hat in Ring emblem on the pocket.

CLASSIC FIGHTERS AIRSHOW

A critical part of the success of the Omaka AHC is the running of the Classic Fighters Airshow every second Easter. These shows actually pre-dated the museum by some years and in fact, before the shows became formal public events, they had their own beginnings with casual 'fly-ins'. These were relaxed gatherings for owners and pilots who wanted to get together to share their aircraft and some flying with like-minded people. Where better to do so that one of the world's last surviving big square grass airfields, and 'smack-dab' in the middle of the country.

The first of these fly-ins was held in February 1995 and focused on vintage machines. Two years later in 1997, Easter became the established weekend and the event was run in conjunction with the New Zealand Warbirds Association. This was hugely successful and saw a great turnout of vintage and warbird aircraft and owners, but also indicated a strong interest from the public who wanted to see what was going on. This was followed by a repeat event over Easter 1999 when the range of participating aircraft grew even more and included our first WW-I machine with Stuart Tantrum's now resident Fokker Triplane.

It became clear at this juncture that public demand was going to require us to provide more access and more facilities such as food and drink outlets, car parking and portable toilets. We really had no choice but to explore the option of holding a formal public-focused airshow.

Tim Sullivan practises for the air show flying the Nieuport 24 along the Marlborough coastline.

Gavin Conroy

As it happened, this was at a time when we'd already been discussing the options for building a museum display for some of the aircraft we had either flying or under rebuild at Omaka. Clearly, the two activities were made for one another and within weeks of the running of the 1999 fly-in, we'd already decided that for 2001, we would hold a full-on International airshow at Omaka over Easter. It would be called, 'Classic Fighters'.

There has always been an unusually strong interest in pre-1920s aircraft at Omaka. As early as 1968, an airshow was held at the field featuring a taxiable replica of the 1909 Bleriot monoplane (which actually flew briefly and quite unexpectedly!). With several members of the community having a strong interest in WW-I aviation, we decided to present a Great War tableau that would include ground troops, a French Chateau set piece, replica WW-I tanks from both sides of the conflict and an observation balloon! Aircraft provided included the late Stuart Tantum's Fokker Triplane, Sir Peter Jackson's Sopwith

Camel, Ed Storo's Bristol Fighter (brought over from Tennessee just for the show) and a static Fokker D.VIII replica built by Chris Boyce and Jay McIntyre. It was clear from the outset that the WW-I theme was going to be very popular with airshow visitors and with that big square all-grass airfield, the Wither Hills 'amphitheatre' and the vineyards as a backdrop, we had the perfect stage on which to perform these displays.

It was particularly pleasing at that first airshow to see the Camel make its 'downunder' flying debut and wearing the freshly applied colours of Blenheim-born Clive Collett, one of New Zealand's significant WW-I 'aces'. Collett achieved 12 victories, all in Sopwith Camels. The Camel is a perennial favourite for airshow visitors and has been at every Classic Fighters Airshow ever since.

Our World War Two component for that first airshow also featured an aircraft imported just for the event, this being Lynette Zuccoli's CAC Boomerang from Toowoomba, Australia, beautifully demonstrated by Nelson-born Wayne Millburn. In addition we were able to feature the Hurricane, Spitfire and Mustang from Wanaka as well as the Kittyhawk and Mustang from Ardmore so the collective assembly of combat aircraft from both world wars certainly supported the 'Classic Fighters' name selected for what proved to be a very successful and highly theatrical event.

The biennial airshow has continued to be a 'work in progress' ever since that first event. Airshows are extremely challenging to run as they require an extraordinary amount of work, huge cooperation from a great many people, and of course, they are reliant on good weather, which adds significant risk to that workload. Each event has however, a significant role to play to support the running of the museum and ultimately the continued growth of the facility. In turn, the museum provides a must-see destination and therefore there is a bonus attraction to ensure extra value is gained for those travelling great distances to attend the show.

A common thread connecting all of the shows held at Omaka to date has been the introduction of theatrical support material that has been used to punctuate the flying displays. This has gone beyond the still present WW-I Chateau and battle sequences, to include such things as the very realistic Eiffel Tower (over 20m – 66 ft tall!) and Arc de Triumph in 2005; Pyramids and Sphinxes in 2003; and in 2009, the monastery at Monte Cassino (50m x 30m x 4 stories built on an adjacent hillside); and even a trio of gondolas which were involved in a nail-biting race along the paddocks of

Venice (you really had to be there….). And then in 2011 there was the V-2 rocket, built full-size by Roger Lauder and his team, and complete with its Meillerwagen launch trailer capable of raising the rocket to its launch height (around 20m once vertical). So realistic was this imposing weapon that once vertical, its rocket motor was started and considerable flames thrust downwards as the giant missile started to raise skywards, reaching a couple of meters in height before being destroyed by strafing Spitfires and Kittyhawks. It's fair to say that the theatre is an important part of the airshow!

Looking towards the future, the airshow model continues to evolve, both in terms of how displays are staged, as well as the financial model ensuring that sufficient value is gained for the AHC from the amount of time and energy that goes into running the show. One of the major benefits that both the airshow and the museum have gained has been the progressive growth in numbers and variety of heritage aircraft that now call Omaka home in concert with the growth in size of the heritage aviation community on

A Bristol Fighter fends off an attack from a Fokker D.VIII, which goes down trailing smoke.

Gavin Conroy

the field. Significant historic machines from both world wars and in between support not just the airshow but also the regular flying days during the summer months and random occasions in between during which you might see a Sopwith Pup and Nieuport out cavorting or a Focke-Wulf 190 or Avro Anson bringing the skies to life over Omaka, or various vintage biplanes taxiing past the museum before heading skywards to show a first-time flier the delights of vintage aviation.

There is no doubt about it: the coupling of the airshow with the AHC is a winning combination and whilst both require vast effort from hundreds of mostly volunteer workers, the enthusiasm is there to ensure that both continue to grow together into the future.

The amazing range of theatrics performed at the Classic Fighters Airshow is exemplified by this image of German troops and vehicles during a ground and air attack that has also seen the destruction of the V-2 rocket just as it was climbing from its launch vehicle.